SERIES 2
THE COMPLETE ORGAN PLAYER SONGBOOK
VOLUME 3

Arranged by Kenneth Baker

Contents

Songs

Wise Publications
London/New York/Sydney/Cologne

Exclusive Distributors:
Music Sales Limited
78 Newman Street, London W1P 3LA, England
Music Sales Pty. Limited
27 Clarendon Street, Artarmon, Sydney, NSW 2064, Australia.

This book © Copyright 1983 by
Wise Publications
UK ISBN 0.7119.0389.1
UK Order No. AM 34083

Music Sales complete catalogue lists thousands of titles
and is free from your local music book shop, or direct from
Music Sales Limited. Please send 30p in stamps for postage to
Music Sales Limited, 78 Newman Street, London W1P 3LA.

Printed in Great Britain
J.B. Offset (Marks Tey) Ltd., Marks Tey, Essex.

REGISTRATION TABLE
(For All Organs)

GENERAL ELECTRONIC ORGANS		DRAWBAR ORGANS	
(1) Upper: Flutes 8′, 4′ Lower: Flute 8′ Pedal: 8′ Vibrato: On (or Leslie: Tremolo)		**(1)** Upper: 00 7604 000 Lower: (00)8600 000(0) Pedal: 4 – (2) Vibrato: On (or Leslie: Tremolo)	
(2) Upper: Vibraphone (or Flute 8′ + Sustain) Lower: Orchestral Strings Pedal: 8′ Vibrato: Off		**(2)** Upper: 00 8600 000 + Sustain Lower: (00)5333 221(0) Pedal: 4 – (2) Vibrato: Off	
(3) Upper: Horn (or Reed 8′) Lower: Flutes 8′, 4′ Pedal: 8′ Vibrato: Off (Leslie: Chorale)		**(3)** Upper: 00 6555 000 Lower: (00)7604 000(0) Pedal: 4 – (2) Vibrato: Off (Leslie: Chorale)	
(4) Upper: Flute 16′, 8′ + Xylophone (or 2′ percussion) Lower: Orchestral Strings Pedal: 16′ + 8′ Vibrato: On (or Leslie: Tremolo)		**(4)** Upper: 80 8004 008 + 2nd Harmonic Lower: (00) 7665 333(0) Pedal: 5 – (3) Vibrato: On (or Leslie: Tremolo)	
(5) Upper: Brass Ensemble Lower: Flutes 8′, 4′ Pedal: 16′ + 8′ Vibrato: On		**(5)** Upper: 66 8555 400 Lower: (00)8604 000(0) Pedal: 5 – (3) Vibrato: On	
(6) Upper: Pan Flute (or Jazz Flute) Lower: Orchestral Strings Pedal: 8′ Vibrato: On		**(6)** Upper: 00 8000 008 Lower: (00)5333 222(0) Pedal: 4 – (2) Vibrato: On	
(7) Upper: Flutes 16′, 8′, 4′ + Piano Lower: Flutes 8′, 4′ Pedal: 16′ + 8′ Vibrato: Off (Leslie: Tremolo with Flutes)		**(7)** Upper: 80 8606 006 + Piano Lower: (00)8800 000(0) Pedal: 5 – (3) Vibrato: Off (Leslie: Tremolo)	
(8) Upper: Flutes 16′, 8′, 4′, 2′ + Orchestral Strings Lower: Flutes 8′, 4′, String 8′ Pedal: 16′ + 8′ Vibrato: On (with Flutes) Off (with Strings)		**(8)** Upper: 85 8355 338 Lower: (00)8833 221(0) Pedal: 6 – (4) Vibrato: On (or Leslie: Tremolo)	

Thank You For The Music

Words & Music: Benny Andersson and Bjorn Ulvaeus

Registration No. ⑤
Suggested Drum Rhythm: **Disco (or Rock)**

Bali Ha'i

Words: Oscar Hammerstein II. Music: Richard Rodgers

NEW CHORD

written:

D+
D
A sharp
F sharp
D pedal

4 (5)   2 (3)   1   (Fingering)

Middle C

Registration No. ②

Suggested Drum Rhythm: **Beguine**

♩ = 92

Ba-li Ha'i may call you an-y night, an-y

day. In your heart you'll hear it call you: "Come a-

way, come a-way" Ba-li Ha'i will

whis-per On the wind of the sea: "Here am

Because Of You

Words & Music: Arthur Hammerstein & Dudley Wilkinson

Registration No. ①
Suggested Drum Rhythm: **Beguine**

What A Wonderful World

Words & Music: George David Weiss and Bob Thiele

What Now My Love

English Words: Carl Sigman. French Lyric: P Delanoe. Music: G Becaud

Registration No. ⑦
Suggested Drum Rhythm: **Slow Rock**

My Favourite Things

Words: Oscar Hammerstein II. Music: Richard Rodgers

JAZZ WALTZ VARIATION

In this variation of the Jazz Waltz rhythm an extra pedal note takes the place of the "split" chord.

As in the earlier versions of the Jazz Waltz given, it is more effective if the Jazz Waltz bars are interspersed with bars of "ordinary" (or other) Waltz rhythms:

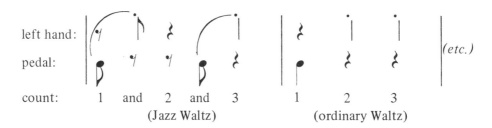

Registration No. ②
Suggested Drum Rhythm: **Jazz Waltz (or Waltz & Beguine)**

Chim Chim Cher-ee

Words & Music: Richard M. Sherman and Robert B. Sherman

Registration No. ④
Suggested Drum Rhythm: **Jazz Waltz (or Waltz & Beguine)**

La Cucaracha

Traditional. Arranged by Kenneth Baker

Registration No. ④
Suggested Drum Rhythm: **Rhumba**

bak - ing ___ Won - dered he "what is she mak - ing?" ___

For it looked so ap - pe - tis - ing ___ with the bat - ter slow - ly

ris - ing ___ To the edge he start - ed skip - ping ___

Then he found that he was slip - ping ___ In the pie so hot and

blaz - in' ___ Now he's just an - oth - er rais - in. La cu - ca -

He's Got The Whole World In His Hands

Traditional. Arranged by Kenneth Baker

Registration No. ⑦
Suggested Drum Rhythm: **Shuffle (or March ⁶⁄₈, or Swing)**

Blue Suede Shoes

Words & Music: Carl Lee Perkins

Registration No. ⑤
Suggested Drum Rhythm: **Swing**

My Blue Heaven

Words: George Whiting. Music: Walter Donaldson

Don't Get Around Much Anymore

Words: Bob Russell. Music: Duke Ellington

This Guy's In Love With You

Words: Hal David. Music: Burt Bacharach

Tuxedo Junction

Words: Buddy Feyne. Music: Erskine Hawkins, William Johnson, Julian Dash

Registration No. ⑧
Suggested Drum Rhythm: **Swing**

For Once In My Life

Words: Ronald Miller. Music: Orlando Murden

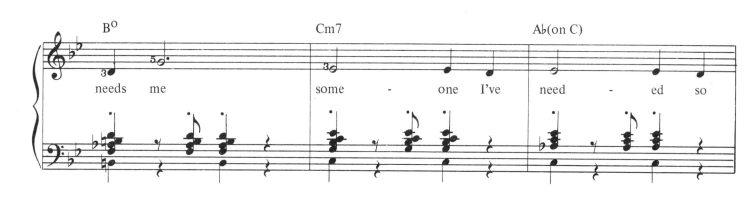

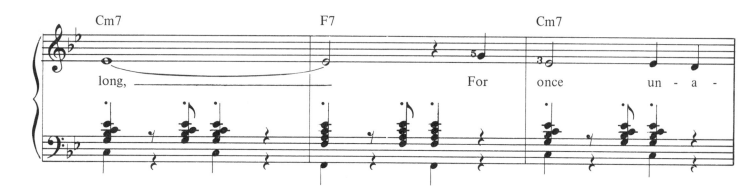

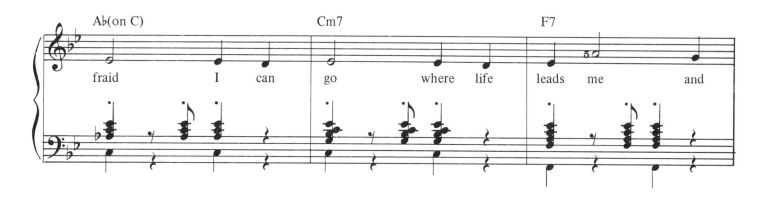

Wave

Words & Music: Antonio Carlos Jobim

Registration No. ⑥
Suggested Drum Rhythm: **Bossa Nova**

* i.e. C#°

first the time was half past three _____ when your eyes met mine it was e - ter - ni - ty. By now we know the wave is on its way to be just catch the wave don't be a - fraid of lov - ing me. The fun - da - men - tal lone - li - ness goes when - ev - er two can dream a dream to - ge - ther. _____

The Coffee Song

Words & Music: Bob Hilliard and Dick Miles

D.%. al Coda   ⊕**CODA**

I Love You And Don't You Forget It

Words: Al Stillman. Music: Henry Mancini

41

42

CHORD CHARTS (For Left Hand)

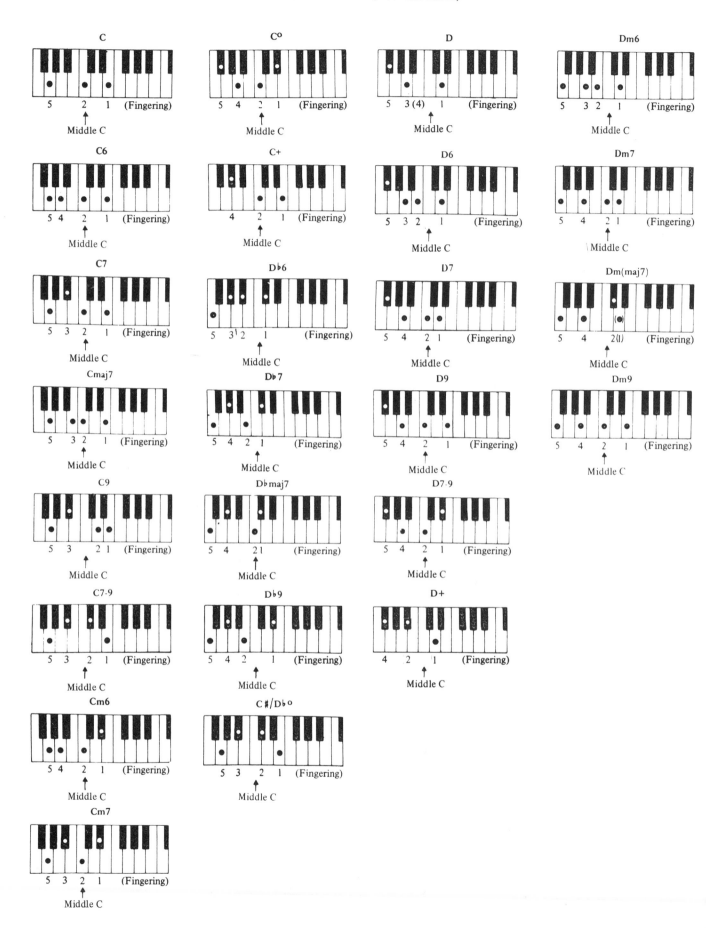

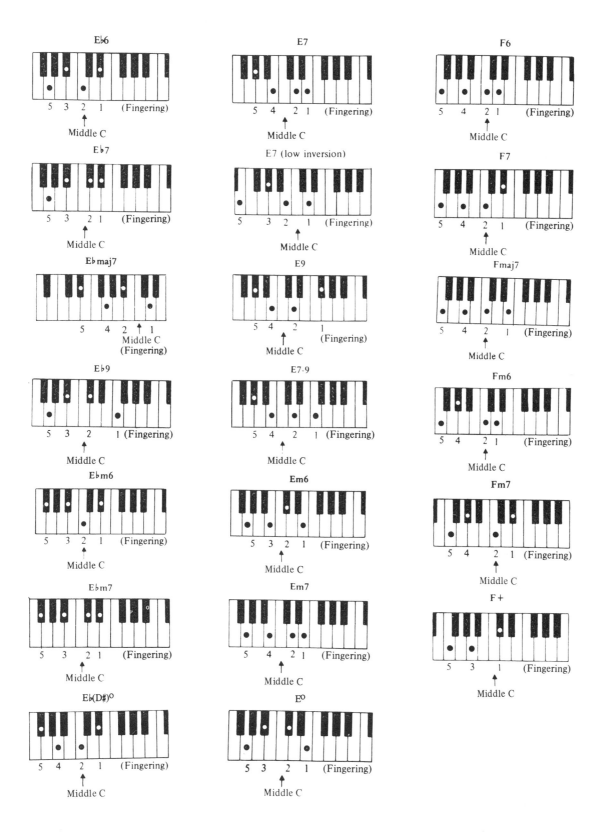

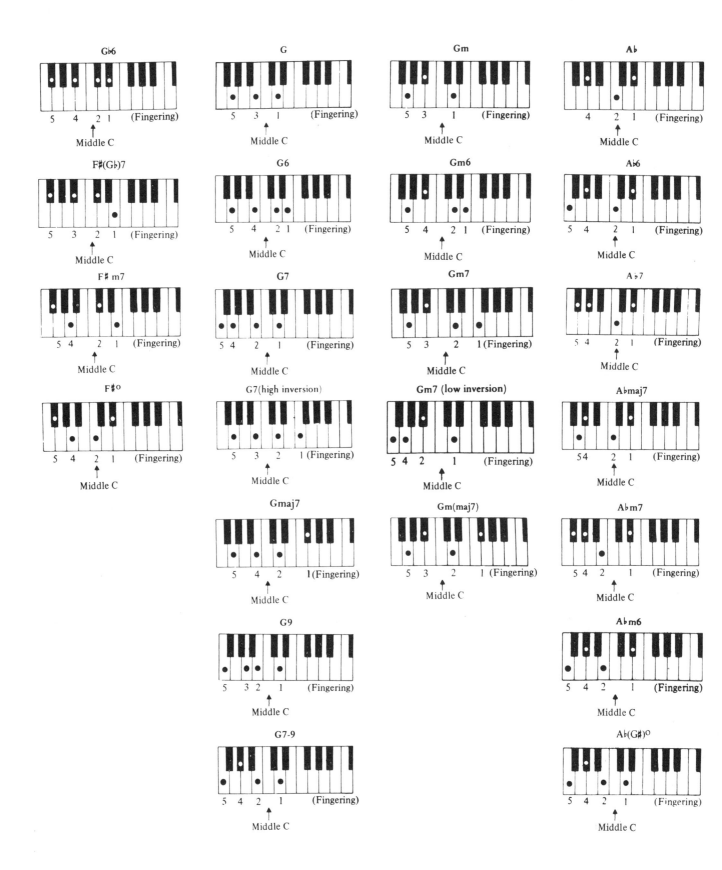

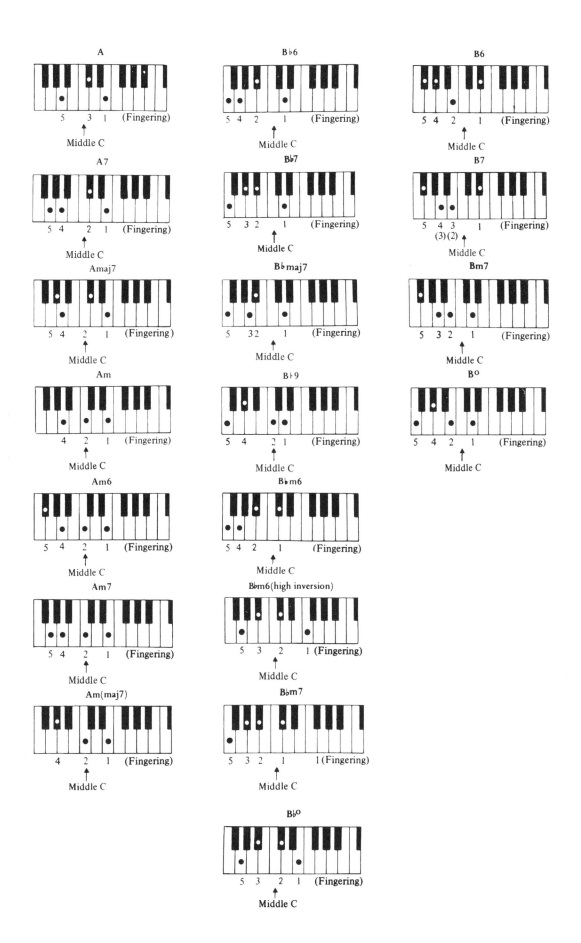

Song Category Index